The Marie Selby Botanical Gardens
"Creating a Passion for Plants"

Mission:

Marie Selby Botanical Gardens passionately
pursues knowledge about tropical plants and
their habitats, and applies that expertise to
advance their conservation and display.

Vision:

Marie Selby Botanical Gardens will be a
recognized world leader in the research,
identification, conservation and display of
epiphytes, especially orchids and bromeliads,
and their canopy ecosystems.

A Passion for Plants

Marie Selby Botanical Gardens

by Jeff LaHurd

Selby Botanical Gardens Press

A Passion for Plants
Marie Selby Botanical Gardens
by Jeff LaHurd

Published June 2001
in an edition of 2,500 copies.

ISBN 0-9701613-2-8

Project Coordinator: Jane Shea

Design by Elsa Kauffman

Published by
Selby Botanical Gardens Press
Sarasota, Florida

Copies of this book are available through
Marie Selby Botanical Gardens
811 South Palm Avenue
Sarasota, Florida 34236 U.S.A.
www.selby.org/research/pubs.htm

Selby Gardens Associates

In the Fall of 1980, a group of seven women decided to form a women's auxiliary for the Marie Selby Botanical Gardens. They were Elaine Baum, Helen Caravelli, Ann Esworthy, Barbara Heller, Mildred Moxley, Virginia Salomon, and Eve Wilkinson. The original intent of the founders was to raise the visibility of the Gardens within the local community. The Associates has evolved into an organization to benefit the Gardens financially by holding special events and social functions.

Members began by launching an ambitious program of holiday events centered at the Christy Payne Mansion. Two years later, the group initiated the Orchid Ball, now a firm fixture on the Sarasota social calendar. The ball is an important fundraiser for the Gardens.

Selby Gardens Associates combine social activities and philanthropy. Over the years, they have actively supported the Gardens through their volunteer efforts and financial contributions.

The Associates celebrated their twentieth anniversary in 2000, and the Gardens commemorated its official twenty-fifth year. The group sponsored this volume to commemorate both milestones.

Kindness in words creates confidence.
Kindness in thinking creates profoundness.
Kindness in giving creates love.

Lao-tzu

Foreword: How Our Garden Grows

With the prediction that more than two thirds of the world's plant species will become extinct during this century, our Selby Gardens oasis is not just a pretty place but an international treasure. *The Marie Selby Botanical Gardens*—those five words conjure up so many different images for each of us... weddings, sunset walks, the enthusiasm of children looking in wonder at an orchid, a new species for the collections, Orchid Ball, Fourth of July with the family, brown-bag lunch seminars, butterfly gardens, canopy walkways, rain forest safaris, bamboo and mangrove walks, banyans, bromeliads in bloom, and great book, museum, and plant shops. So many thoughts and moments comprise the history of Selby Gardens, but what we cannot see on the grounds is perhaps our greatest treasure—the legacy of scientists who have created the illustrious international reputation of Selby Gardens. Selby may be "the supernova in the constellation of gardens," but it is also a galaxy in the world of tropical botanical research. Our scientists have led expeditions for more than 25 years, and they, their discoveries, and their publications span the globe. These behind-the-scenes achievements create a strong base upon which Selby Gardens may grow and flower in this new century as a major force in conservation, both local and international.

The Selby Associates have worked long and hard to create this volume as a special anniversary tribute to the Gardens. Over its 25 year history, the Gardens has been blessed with the energy and many projects achieved by the Selby Associates.

The volume presented here pays tribute to past and present people and plants of Selby Gardens, all essential components of our special green oasis in downtown Sarasota. Enjoy!

Margaret Lowman, Ph.D.
Executive Director
May 2001

Acknowledgments

My sincere thanks go to those whose help made this book possible: Nathalie McCulloch and Jane Shea of Selby Gardens Associates, and Dr. Meg Lowman, Dr. George Bañez, Bruce Holst, Harry Luther, Shirley Thompson, Tom Roberts and Barry Walsh of the Selby Gardens staff. I appreciate my personal guided tour of the Gardens hosted by Ann Esworthy. Her commentary about Marie Selby and the Gardens was most helpful.

I received information for this book from Selby Gardens staff members, the comprehensive Selby Gardens web pages, and numerous Selby Gardens *Bulletins.* Jane Shea gathered much of the material I used for research and helped with choosing the photographs and compiling the chronology. I also received information from an article by Charlie Huisking published in the *Sarasota Herald-Tribune.*

As this is primarily a pictorial of one of Sarasota's loveliest settings, I would like to thank the photographers whose pictures enhance this book: Thomas Balaÿ, Wally Berg, Elaine Dunkelberger, Bruce Holst, Stephen Ingram, Margarette Mead, Francisco Oliva-Esteva, Stan Pastor, Vern Sawyer, Bob Wands, and Bill West. Their photography is stunningly beautiful.

The elegant illustrations in this volume were created by the artist, Stig Dalström.

I thank Nancy Wilke for her help in editing this volume.

Jeff LaHurd

"I do not understand how anyone can live without one small place of enchantment to turn to."

Marjorie Kinnan Rawlings

isis schilleriana.
alaÿ

Orchids, the largest plant family in the world, are mostly epiphytes—plants that live upon other plants without being parasites. *Laelia purpurata* var. *werkhauseri*, pictured here, is such an orchid. Epiphyte research and display is a specialty at Selby Gardens.

a passion for plants

Amid the hustle of today's Sarasota, within the very city limits of a thriving community known for unceasing growth and the turmoil that is a by-product of ongoing construction, lies a 13-acre island of beauty and tranquility.

This is the Marie Selby Botanical Gardens, gifted by Marie Selby, long-time Sarasota resident and philanthropist, "to serve the people of Sarasota as a beautiful and peaceful garden where one may enjoy the splendor of the plant world in one of the most lovely settings in Florida."

Bordered on Palm Avenue by Sarasota Bay and Hudson Bayou, Selby Gardens has evolved into a multifaceted, renowned center of scientific research, conservation, education, and display—a "must-see" destination for visitors from around the world.

the selbys

In many ways, the grounds of the Marie Selby Botanical Gardens are a microcosm of the Sarasota that so captivated Marie Selby when she arrived here with her husband William in 1909—a pristine subtropical paradise where the glories of nature were the primary attractions. Even the quaint, shaded, red-brick avenue that leads to the Gardens is a throwback to more peaceful times.

Vern Sawyer

Aechmea kentii, a member of the bromeliad family, which also includes pineapples and Spanish moss. Approximately two-thirds of all bromeliads are epiphytic, but the best known, the pineapple, is terrestrial.

Sarasota was still an out-of-the-way community of fewer than one thousand souls in those days. Hard to reach, it was an outdoorsman's delight. The woods were full of game, the Gulf of Mexico and Sarasota Bay were pristine and teeming with all manner of fish. Bill

3

Selby was an avid hunter and fisherman, and Marie, who also loved to fish, often joined him. Both fell in love with Sarasota and would make it their permanent winter residence for the remainder of their lives.

Initially, the Selbys lived on a houseboat moored at the foot of Main Street, but they soon built a small Spanish Mediterranean style home on a peninsula bordered by Sarasota Bay and Hudson Bayou. The Selbys were wealthy, having made a fortune in the oil business before Selby Oil and Gas Company became a part of Texaco, yet they led an unpretentious life style. Even during the freewheeling 1920s, when Gatsby-esque glitz and glamour among the wealthy were commonplace, neither the reticent Marie nor the more gregarious Bill flaunted their wealth. That was never their style.

Eager shoppers hunt for the perfect plant at a Selby Gardens Plant Fair. Plant fairs are held in the spring and fall each year.

Bill was considered something of a local character. He was a big man, partial to cowboy boots and casual clothes—a downtown regular who enjoyed large cigars and kibitzing with the locals at the Badger's Drug Store coffee counter. Most never guessed that he was a millionaire several times over; but shortly before he died, this unaffected multi-millionaire, frugal during his lifetime, would become one of the most well known benefactors in the community's history. The Selby name would become synonymous with philanthropy in Sarasota. The Selby Foundation, a perpetual trust, was established by Bill and Marie Selby to assist educational and charitable projects. It has blossomed to benefit the community and numerous local non-profit organizations.

Marie Minshall Selby was a unique woman. Having attended a music seminary, she was an accomplished pianist and frequently relaxed by playing her piano. Although a

Elaine Dunkelberger

Heliconia wagneriana. Heliconias grow from underground rhizomes and were long classified as part of the banana family, but they are more closely related to the bird-of-paradise family. Most grow in humid areas of the New World tropics. They are pollinated by hummingbirds attracted to their brightly colored inflorescences.

homebody who spent many hours gardening, she was also the first woman to travel across the United States by automobile (she accompanied Bill), when such a journey was more a perilous adventure than a vacation trip. In her youth, she often accompanied her geologist father on camping trips. She had a fondness for horses and loved horseback riding. When Bill bought 3,000 acres of property east of town to raise beef, Marie kept a stable of horses at the ranch. It was often remarked that she dressed casually, even when shopping, probably because she was either on her way to or from a ride.

Her love of flowers and the influence of their beauty led to her membership in the Founders Circle of the Sarasota Garden Club. The group formed in 1927 to beautify the community, which was suffering the deleterious effects of the real estate crash, by planting flowers.

Marie Selby died on June 17, 1971, at the age of 81. By the time of her death, she had extended her original homestead to seven acres, having purchased two acres to the north to protect it from development. Palmer Bank, as executor of her estate, announced that she had left her property and an endowment for the establishment of a botanical garden that could be used by local clubs for meetings and social events.

A tranquil spot on the South Lawn.

the early years of the gardens

The directors of the Palmer Bank were not enthusiastic about the creation of a true botanical garden. Fortunately, the energetic bank chairman, William Coleman, was receptive to the potential of the property as described by a fellow board member, Dr. Carlyle A. Luer. Dr. Luer was an orchid enthusiast and author of *The Native Orchids of Florida*. In the summer of 1972, it was decided to go ahead with the establishment of the Marie Selby Botanical Gardens, with the focus on epiphytic plants. Dr. Luer would become a director during the development of the Gardens, designer of its first logo, founding editor of the research journal, *Selbyana*, and tireless board member.

Tillandsia fasciculata variety *densispica*. The bromeliad family contains about 2,700 tropical American species that have a broad range from deserts to equatorial rain forests. Only one species, *Pitcairnia feliciana*, is native to an area outside of the Americas, and it is found in tropical West Africa.

7

The next step was to recruit an executive director. In January 1973, William Coleman and Dr. Luer offered the job to Dr. Calaway H. Dodson, a professor of botany at the University of Miami and curator of its herbarium. He arrived in Sarasota with his family in March 1973, moved into the second floor of Selby House, which also was used as an office, and began the herculean task of helping to transform Bill and Marie Selby's property into the Marie Selby Botanical Gardens.

In a talk at the Cooley Theater on April 10, 2000, Dr. Dodson recalled that one of the early rules at the Gardens was that no staff person had a special position—everyone was a worker. And there was a great deal of work to do. Tons of trash, underbrush, and invasive trees and foliage needed to be hauled away. The volunteer program, which has been a major factor in the ongoing success of the Gardens, was formed early on. High school students were recruited to help construct the walkways, install the sprinkler system, and do much of the heavy work. As the orchids would need protection, construction of a 14,000 square foot greenhouse was a priority.

Professor Herrick Smith, head of the University of Florida Landscaping Department, was

Paphiopedilum rothschildianum, Asian slipper orchid found only on serpentine rock formations on the slc of Mt. Kinabalu, Borneo. Because of its large bloom and spectacular color, this orchid is a popular specie for hybridization.

consulted on the layout for the Gardens. Kiat Tan, then a graduate student of Dr. Dodson, was responsible for much of the physical look of the Gardens, which Dr. Dodson credits to Tan's "Chinese sense of balance and harmony."

The epiphytic plant collections at Selby Gardens originated from the private collections of the early members of the scientific staff. Dr. Dodson, Dr. Luer, and Dr. Tan donated their collections of orchids, and Dr. Hans Wiehler provided his extensive collection of New World gesneriads.

By the spring of 1974, in addition to a greenhouse, the Gardens boasted a herbarium, had acquired the stately Christy Payne Mansion for use as an administration building, and had an active volunteer group. It was noted in the Gardens newsletter, *The Bulletin*, that Selby Gardens was not a tourist attraction, but rather a place to serve the people of Sarasota as a beautiful and peaceful garden where they could enjoy the splendors of the plant world. Soon it would become known around the world for its scientific research.

After two years of hard work and community anticipation, the Marie Selby Botanical Gardens was officially opened to the public on July 7, 1975, and $1 admission was charged. The following year, on April 3, an appropriately bright day, a large crowd gathered for the formal dedication. Guests included local dignitaries and international plant experts. The keynote speaker, Dr. Peter H. Raven, director of the Missouri Botanical Garden, who would later be named a *Time* Magazine Hero of the Planet, marveled at "the unbelievable progress" the staff had made and told the audience, "This is an exciting occasion for the botanical community around the world."

Bruce Holst

"*Just living is not enough…*
one must have sunshine, freedom,
and a little flower."

Hans Christian Andersen

Bambusa oldhamii, giant timber b...
Bi

a stroll through the grounds

The Marie Selby Botanical Gardens houses the world's most outstanding collection of living epiphytes or "air plants." A stroll through the grounds offers an array of distinctive groves, displays, walkways, and gardens designed in a manner that envelopes the visitor in the beauty and serenity of nature.

Vern Sawyer

The Tropical Display House where plants are displayed at the peak of their bloom. Here is the most concentrated collection of epiphytic plants in the United States.

The tone for a tour of the grounds is set at the Tropical Display House. Here visitors enter a wonderland of native and exotic flora and imagine themselves in a lush tropical rain forest. Treasures displayed here originate from all over the tropical world and include torch ginger from Indonesia, colorful Amazonian bromeliads, strange, carnivorous pitcher plants from Borneo, palms from the Seychelles, heliconias from Ecuador, the vanilla orchid from Mexico, and other spectacular orchids from many places, including Florida. The Tropical Display House holds the most concentrated collection of epiphytic plants in the United States.

The adjacent Fernery showcases select epiphytic members of the world's 10,000 species of ferns. More than one-third of all ferns live as epiphytes, and some genera, such as the ones in the Fernery, are exclusively epiphytic. Popular staghorns are well represented. Staghorn ferns grow naturally in tropical Africa, Madagascar, and the islands of the Indian Ocean to China, the Philippines, and eastern Australia, and one species is found in South America.

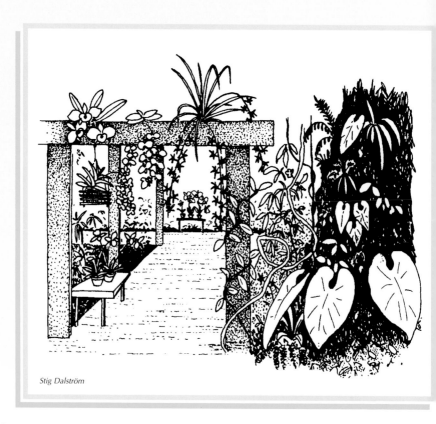

Stig Dalström

Stan Pastor

A Jain statue from the Sarna Collection with hibiscus blossoms.

The collections continue outside, exhibited in the 8.5 acres that make up the display gardens. Cycads, ferns, and bromeliads growing in the trellis area and grove adjacent to the Tropical Display House delight the visitor. Look for the collection of statuary, drums, and bells donated by the Sarna family.

Cycads, ancient plants similar to palms and tree ferns, actually are related to neither. Remotely related to the conifers, they grow in the tropics and subtropics around the world. These are slow-growing, globally endangered exotic plants that live for centuries if undisturbed, but today in many areas they are threatened by land clearing and illegal collection.

Stig Dalström

Visitors should look up, look down, and all around. Bromeliads adorn the branches and understories of trees throughout the Gardens, as well as rocks on the ground. Spanish moss and pineapples are two well-known examples of the bromeliad family. Most bromeliads are native to the New World, and 16 species are native to Florida.

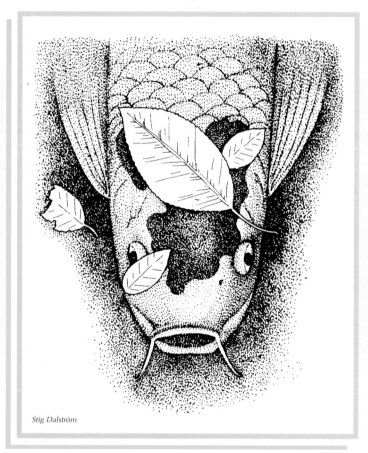

Stig Dalström

Behind Selby House, one passes the Live Oak Grove. These magnificent trees were present when Mrs. Selby lived in the house. Overhead, ferns, aroids, Spanish moss, and other bromeliads perch on the branches. Underneath the oak canopy grow Australian tree ferns with their lacy foliage.

Vern Sawyer

The Koi Pond and Waterfall form one of the loveliest and most tranquil sites in the Gardens. A smidgen of imagination makes visitors feel far from the madding crowd.

Australian tree ferns also grow around the Koi Pond and Waterfall arden. This lovely, tranquil setting is surrounded by water-loving lants such as exotic heliconias, angel's trumpet, elephant ears, and ald cypress which is native to Florida. The pond supports a population f elegant Japanese koi fish.

Nearing Selby House, one passes the Bamboo Pavilion. A member of the grass family, the giant timber bamboo from China can grow to a height of 60 feet with stems more than three inches in diameter. Bamboos are extremely fast-growing plants, and one variety may grow as much as four feet in a single day.

A bench for quiet respite at the Bamboo Pavilion.

Selby House today houses the Selby Gardens Book & Gift Shop, a classroom, and an apartment for visiting scientists. The impressive Banyan Grove in front of Selby House was planted by Mrs. Selby's gardener, Grover Yancy, in 1937. Mr. Yancy continued to work on the property when it became Selby Gardens and until his retirement in June 1992. The Banyan Grove has a plaque in his honor.

Selby House, the Spanish Mediterranean style home of William and Marie Selby, today houses the Selby Gardens Book & Gift Shop, a classroom, and a visiting scientist's apartment.

Distinguished by their spreading aerial roots, banyans are members of the fig family, and native to both Africa and tropical Asia. They are widely cultivated throughout south Florida.

lable banyans shade a statue of the Thinker. Mrs. Selby was fond of the fig family. She planted six species, ing the Banyan Grove and the Bo Tree at the end of the peninsula.

Stig Dalström

On the banks of Hudson Bayou and adjacent to the Banyan Grove is Walker's Walk. This is the world's first wheelchair-accessible canopy walkway, and it allows the disabled, as well as young children in strollers, to experience tree top exploration. The walkway was constructed in 1999, and the dedication festivities coincided with the tenth anniversary of the Americans with Disabilities Act. At certain times of the year, visitors can catch a glimpse of manatees frolicking in the bayou.

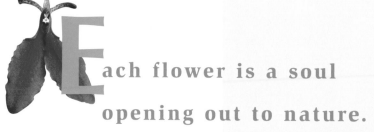

Each flower is a soul

opening out to nature.

Gerald de Nerval

The walkway bordering Hudson Bayou wanders past the Hibiscus Garden and Succulent Garden. Award-winning hibiscus plants flower throughout the year. Blooms can be up to 10 inches across, and hybrid varieties range in color from nearly black through brown and lavender to the more familiar red, yellow, and pink. Often referred to as the Florida rose, the hibiscus is a member of the mallow family.

ful hibiscus, one of Florida's showiest landscape plants.

The Succulent Garden provides a sharp contrast to the lush vegetation that surrounds it. Cacti are native only to the Americas, while succulents, so named because they store water, are found around the world. Some succulents even grow in the arid environment of the upper rain forest canopy. Aloe vera, a member of the lily family, is well-known for its use in treating burns. Oil extracted from the jojoba plant is used to manufacture lubricants, cosmetics, and other products once made from sperm whale oil.

Farther along the path, one encounters the Wildflower Garden featuring such southern species as echinacea, goldenrod, and beach sunflower. Most are Florida natives and can tolerate hot weather and drought condi-

The Succulent Garden. A succulent plant has thick, juicy, f leaves and/or stems, often an adaptation to an arid climate common succulents include aloe, agave, yucca, kalanchoe, most cacti.

tions. The Gazebo, covered with colorful vines, is a popular spot for weddings. The large lawn between the Gazebo and Selby House is often used for special events, including plant fairs, wedding receptions, and the annual Orchid Ball, a major fundraiser for the Gardens.

Vern Sawyer

The Wildflower Garden is home to such species as echinacea, mistflower, and beach sunflower. Some are Florida natives well adapted to sun and sand.

Nowhere along the stroll is the contrast between the then and
ow of Sarasota, or perhaps between Mother Nature and modern
1an, more apparent than at the point of the peninsula near the
iazebo. Standing on the shell shoreline, gazing across the lovely
/aters of Sarasota Bay with the tranquility of the Selby Gardens land-
cape to the rear, one faces a panorama of distant traffic, high-rise
uildings, bridges, boats of every size, and housing developments.
his view may make one more appreciative of Selby Gardens.

Situated on the South Lawn, surrounded by flowers and facing Sarasota Bay, the Gazebo is one of several
picturesque sites for wedding ceremonies at the Gardens.

A visit to the Gardens is enhanced by the unobtrusive but inform-
tive markers that not only identify plants but provide some of their
istory. The Bo Tree is, one learns, sacred to Buddhists and Hindus
ecause Buddha, after meditating under such a tree for nearly six
ears, was said to have received his enlightenment. Close by, the
narker in front of a gumbo limbo tree tells that the tree is also known
s the Tourist Tree because its bark is red and peeling.

21

Stig Dalström

Beyond the Gazebo is the Baywalk, a sanctuary o red, black, and white mangroves. Found from St. Augustine south around the Florida peninsula, mangroves grow along salt water shores and provide breeding grounds for birds fish, and other small marine animals. Silver buttonwood and seagrape grow in the drier zone behind the mangroves. One can stand here for hours and marvel at the synergistic relationships of the sea and its plant and animal life.

Bruce Holst

Rhizophora mangle, red mangrove. Mangroves colonize mud flats, and their debris-catching root systems help stabilize shorelines. They provide a nursery for vulnerable marine animals, including 25 percent of gulf seafood consumed by humans.

Bruce Holst

bium lindleyi. Orchids are found in nearly every part of the world, from arctic regions to the tropics and 2a level up to 14,000 feet. The majority of orchid species, however, flourish in tropical regions.

Leaving the Baywalk and back on the sidewalk, visitors are only a ew steps from the Canopy Platform. Look high into the treetops and ,ee a platform similar to those used by scientists when they conduct esearch in the forest canopies of the world. The platform also is used or demonstrating rope climbing techniques developed for canopy ιccess.

Stig Dalström

To the west of Selby House, visitors pass the Palm Grove. Nearly 100 palm species are grown in the Gardens, including date, fishtail, triangle, saw palmetto, and Florida's state tree, the cabbage palm. Many of the world's 2,600 species of palms grow in dense understories of rain forests, but some live in deserts, and a few range as far north as coastal North Carolina and Southern Europe and as far south as New Zealand. Besides their value as ornamentals, palms produce dates, coconuts, oils, waxes, and building materials.

Stroll along the Bayfront Garden planted with salt-tolerant plants and past the Activities Center, which is booked year-round for both public and private events. The terrace is a favorite sunset-viewing

A view of Sarasota's bay front from Selby Gardens.

spot. Continue along the path to the Shoreline Restoration behind the Christy Payne Mansion. This picturesque area demonstrates a successful coastal wetlands remediation project. An extremely diverse and colorful collection of native plants, ranging from freshwater to salt-

Stig Dalström

water tolerant, surrounds a lagoon and helps filter runoff before it reaches Sarasota Bay. The area regularly attracts a variety of water birds such as the great blue heron, snowy egret, and yellow crowned night heron. These wading birds hunt for aquatic creatures along the shore and among the mangroves.

Now it's on to the Payne Mansion. This gorgeous colonial style residence was built by a friend of the Selbys, fellow oilman and

Bruce Holst

approach to the lovely Christy Payne Mansion from the south.

fishing partner, Christy Payne, in 1934 as a retirement home for himself and his wife, Anne. They moved here in August 1935. The home cost $50,000 during the Great Depression. Payne, a historic mansion buff, incorporated into his home design features from mansions he had visited and sketched over the years.

Dr. and Mrs. James Paulk purchased the mansion in 1964, and they lived there until 1973 when they sold it to the Marie Selby Botanical Gardens with the understanding that it would become a part of the Gardens.

The elegant Christy Payne Mansion has become the Gardens hallmark. Payne, a historic mansion buff and Selby friend, built the house in 1934 as his retirement home. Today it features the Museum Shop, exhibits, and special events.

The distinguished residence, listed on the National Register of Historic Places, is the hallmark of the grounds. After serving as the administrative center and staff offices, it became the Selby Museum of Botany and the Arts in 1979. The Museum Shop features art and photography of a botanic nature with representative works of local artists.

Stephen Ingram

Tillandsia ionantha, the blushing-bride tillandsia from Central America.

The mansion, featured on the Sarasota Distinguished Homes Tour, has been chosen as a Symphony Associates Designer Showcase House on several occasions. Extensive renovations to the exterior were made in the winter of 2000.

Stig Dalström

The Butterfly Garden is across from the entrance to the Christy Payne Mansion. Its colorful flowers attract several varieties of butterflies searching for nectar and a source of food for their larvae. Some of the plants in the area are milkweeds, lantanas, cassias, passion vines, and salvias. Swallowtails, monarchs, fritillaries, buckeyes, and Florida's zebra longwing butterfly may be found in various stages of development.

A carriage house that sits adjacent to the Payne Mansion today houses the Tree Lab, an educational "hands-on" experience that promotes conservation awareness. The Tree Lab is used extensively as an instructional resource for the Selby Gardens school program. The Gardens also offers summer camps for children and other educational opportunities for children and adults, including basic "how-to" classes for gardeners and art classes using botanical subjects as a theme.

In joy or sadness, flowers
are our constant friends.

Kozuko Okakura

28

Bruce Holst

Amorphophallus titanum, the titan arum, has the world's largest unbranched inflorescence. An aroid, the titan arum was first discovered by Europeans in Sumatra, Indonesia, in 1878. This plant is not only remarkable for the size of its inflorescence, but also for its fetid aroma. Many species of *Amorphophallus* attract pollinating insects with the smell of rotting flesh. Two titan arums bloomed at Selby Gardens in May 1999.

Turn round the corner and enter the Herb Garden to find herbs and spices that may be easily grown in the subtropics. Throughout the year, visitors may find an allspice tree, a curry leaf tree, Cuban oregano, and many other species. Because of the abundance of these plants and their tempting aroma, visitors may carefully touch and taste the herbs and spices in this demonstration garden.

The Tropical Food Garden is a treat. Here grow a cornucopia of edible staples from all over the world. They include the luffa vine, whose fruit is edible in its early growth, but luffa is more commonly known for the fibrous remains of its fruit used as an exfoliant sponge by bathers. Spinach from Ceylon, sweet potato from tropical America, and edible hibiscus from Asia may also be found here. Depending on the growing season, look for pineapples, papayas, plantains, bananas, sugar cane, and other fruits and vegetables considered staples in tropical countries.

Before exiting the Gardens, the visitor should browse in the Plant Shop which is brimming with beautiful orchids, bromeliads, and hundreds of tropical plants for indoor decorating and outdoor landscaping.

Behind the scenes at Selby Gardens. The living research collection of more than 12,000 plants is housed under 20,755 sq. ft. of greenhouse space. When specimens come into flower they are loaned to the Tropical Display House for the enjoyment of visitors.

research and conservation

While the lovely grounds offer the main attraction for visitors, behind the scenes, the Marie Selby Botanical Gardens undertakes serious scientific research into epiphytic plants and their canopy ecosystems. Since its founding, Selby Gardens has participated in more than 150 expeditions to most of the tropical and subtropical regions of the world to conduct research and collect plants. The National Science Foundation, Earthwatch, and the National Geographic Society are among the groups that help fund these expeditions.

Thomas Balay

Paphiopedilum malipoense, a rare and endangered lady slipper orchid from China, is maintained in the living research collection.

Selby Gardens scientists explore for new plants in Ecuador. Staff botanists discover and name hundreds of plant species new for science. Botanical research at Selby Gardens provides critical information needed to understand and conserve life on earth.

Research opportunities in the field of tropical epiphytic taxonomy and canopy biology are unlimited. The Gardens plant collections, living and preserved, are well documented with many entered into a computer database. In addition, the Research Library houses thousands of books and scientific journals. A rare book collection includes botanical works dating to the 1700s. *Selbyana*, the journal of the Marie Selby Botanical Gardens, publishes original research of staff members as well as that of leading epiphyte and canopy scientists from around the world. In 1999, Selby Gardens inaugurated Selby Botanical Gardens Press, which publishes *Selbyana*, plant field guides, and other botanical books and periodicals. In 2000, the Center for Canopy Ecology opened as the only such center at a botanical garden.

Base camp in the Maya Mountains of Belize photographed during a tropical downpour.
Archaeologists working in Belize invited Selby Gardens scientists to study plants that might have
been used by the ancients.

Well known within the scientific community are the Selby
Gardens Orchid Identification Center (OIC) and the Mulford B.
Foster Bromeliad Identification Center (BIC). The OIC was initially
funded in 1975 on a trial basis by the American Orchid Society,

A tropical rain forest canopy as seen from an elevated walkway in Amazonian Peru. Rain forest
canopies are home to a rich abundance and diversity of life. At such sites, Selby Gardens Center
for Canopy Ecology studies intricate interactions between canopy organisms and their environment.

Brocchinia tatei, a bromeliad known only from the Lost World region of Venezuela. Selby Gardens botanists are helping to prepare a 9-volume treatise on Lost World plants.

Francisco Oliva-Esteva

and the BIC in 1978 was named in honor of one of the world's leading bromeliad collectors. Each center has collected a wealth of reference information, and each year together provide more than 800 plant identifications for institutions and individuals.

...ia holstii. This bromeliad was discovered and collected by one Selby staff member and described as a ...species for science by another. The plant was found on a remote mountain range in Peru during a ...ervation International Rapid Assessment Program (RAP) expedition. Such expeditions study biodiverse ...threatened by development. RAP reports document for conservation and government land-use planners ...iological value of an area.

The identification of new plants is facilitated by the Selby Gardens Herbarium. Plants collected on field expeditions are sent to the Herbarium, where they are dried and mounted, and identified by taxonomists. The Herbarium, which began with 3,000 specimens from the private collection of Dr. Calaway Dodson, has grown to more than 84,000 specimens. Known worldwide as SEL, the Herbarium is open for study to visiting scientists and students, and specimens from its collections are loaned to institutions here and abroad.

Vern Sawyer

Volunteers mounting dried plant specimens on archival quality paper for deposit in the Selby Gardens Herbarium. Well-preserved herbarium specimens can last hundreds of years.

A person who cares about the earth will resonate with its purity.

Sally

Selby Gardens provides an opportunity for future scientists through its Internship Program. During a 3-month period, interns participate in hands-on learning experiences in subtropical horticulture, environmental education, taxonomic and ecological research, and the management of nonprofit organizations.

Ceratostemma sylvicola. An epiphytic member of the blueberry family. Epiphytic species are found in more than 80 plant families, including the nightshade, aroid, cactus, and begonia families.

Nature uses as little as possible.

Johannes Kepler

In education and research programs, Selby Gardens stresses the need to preserve native plants, such as the cab palm and seagrape shown here growing on the shores of nearby Longboat Key.

Students are provided with on-site housing and a daily food allowance. The Internship Program draws participants from around the world. Many graduates of the program go on to leadership roles at Selby Gardens and other botanical institutions around the world.

dsia pruinosa, a bromeliad rare in the Florida wild grows at Selby Gardens, where the Mulford B. Foster
liad Identification Center is the world's leading site for bromeliad studies.

Sunset at Selby Gardens during Selby by Candlelight, an annual celebration of the holiday season with music
luminarias.

 arie and William Selby would undoubtedly be
proud of the many accomplishments made
through the years by Marie's namesake gardens.
For while their property has grown and flourished, it has

maintained its original beauty; and while the Marie Selby
Botanical Gardens is now heralded internationally, it has
remained true to Marie Selby's original objective, to serve the
people of Sarasota as a peaceful garden, a place to enjoy the
splendors of the plant world.

CHRONOLOGY

June 17, 1971   Longtime Sarasota resident and benefactor Marie Minshall Selby dies.

June 1972   Palmer Bank announces the provision in Mrs. Selby's will to establish a botanical garden in Sarasota.

November 1972   William Coleman, president of the Palmer Bank, proceeds with the establishment of a botanical garden after consultation with the New York Botanical Garden, the University of Miami, and the University of Florida.

January 1973   The trustees of Mrs. Selby's estate agree to ask Dr. Caloway Dodson to accept the position as the first executive director of the Gardens.

June 1973   The Gardens purchases the Payne House. It is used as the administration building.

Spring 1974   Construction of a complex of four greenhouses is completed. Friends of the Gardens, a membership organization, is launched to support the Marie Selby Botanical Gardens.

Summer 1974	Construction of the interior of the Tropical Display House is completed. The current administration building is purchased for use as a temporary science building.
December 1974	Friends of the Gardens participates in the first formal preview of the Gardens.
Spring 1975	The first issue of *Selbyana*, the Journal of the Marie Selby Botanical Gardens, is published.
Summer 1975	The Orchid Identification Center is set up on a one-year trial basis.
July 7, 1975	The Marie Selby Botanical Gardens is opened to the public. Admission charge is $1.
April 3, 1976	The formal dedication of Selby Gardens takes place.
December 17, 1976	The 1,000th membership in the Gardens is purchased.
November 1978	The Bromeliad Identification Center is established, and named in honor of Mulford B. Foster, a famous collector.

Spring 1979	Administration moves from the Payne Mansion across Palm Avenue to its current location to accommodate the first Symphony Designers Showcase to be held at Selby Gardens.
Summer 1979	The Museum of Botany and the Arts is established at the Payne Mansion.
1979	Selby Gardens Associates, the women's auxiliary, is formed.
April 1982	The first Orchid Ball, a major fundraiser for Selby Gardens, is sponsored by Selby Gardens Associates.
September 1985	The First International Epiphyte Symposium is held at Selby Gardens.
May 1987	Cooley Visitor Reception Center is dedicated.
Winter 1988	The Baywalk is opened.
April 16, 1989	The Activities Center is opened.
May 1991	The Second International Epiphyte Symposium is held at Selby Gardens.

Summer 1991	The Selby Gardens Stark Botanical Research Center is opened at 711 South Palm Avenue.
Fall 1992	Grover Yancy, Mrs. Selby's gardener, retires.
Summer 1993	The Payne Mansion carriage house is converted into the Learning Center. Today it is known as the Tree Lab.
Summer 1994	The first canopy platform in any botanical garden in the world is opened.
Fall 1994	The First International Forest Canopy Conference is held at Selby Gardens.
June 1997	An Orchid Conservation Symposium takes place at Selby Gardens.
December 1997	Selby by Candlelight is inaugurated.
Spring 1998	Selby Gardens receives accreditation by the American Association of Museums.
September 25, 1998	The Christy Payne Mansion is listed on the National Register of Historic Places.

Fall 1998	The Second International Forest Canopy Conference is held at Selby Gardens.
Spring 1999	Two titan arums, with unbranched inflorescences thought to be the largest in the world, bloom simultaneously, attracting hordes of media and visitors to Selby Gardens.
Summer 1999	The first wheelchair-accessible canopy walkway in the world is opened.
Winter 1999	Selby Botanical Gardens Press is launched.
July 2000	Selby Gardens begins its official twenty-fifth anniversary year.
September 1, 2000	The Center for Canopy Ecology opens at Selby Gardens.
Winter 2000	Historical restoration of the exterior of the Christy Payne Mansion is completed.

Executive Directors of Selby Botanical Gardens

1973 – 1981   Calaway Dodson, Ph.D.

1981 – 1988   General George C. Loving

1988 – 1994   Larry Pardue

1994 – 1999   Mark W. Bierner, Ph.D.

1999 – present   Margaret D. Lowman, Ph.D.

A Glossary of Plants mentioned in
A Passion for Plants

Common Name	Scientific Name	Plant family
Agave	*Agave* species	Agavaceae
Allspice	*Pimenta dioica*	Myrtaceae
Aloe vera	*Aloe barbadensis*	Liliaceae
Angel's trumpet	*Brugmansia versicolor*	Solanaceae
Australian tree fern	*Sphaeropteris cooperi*	Cyatheaceae
Banana	*Musa x paradisiaca*	Musaceae
Banyan	*Ficus* species	Moraceae
Beach sunflower	*Helianthus debilis*	Asteraceae
Bo tree	*Ficus religiosa*	Moraceae
Bromeliads		
	Aechmea biflora	Bromeliaceae
	Aechmea kentii	Bromeliaceae
	Brocchinia tatei	Bromeliaceae
	Pepinia holstii	Bromeliaceae
	Pitcairnia feliciana	Bromeliaceae
	Tillandsia fasciculata variety *densispica*	Bromeliaceae
	Tillandsia ionantha	Bromeliaceae
	Tillandsia pruinosa	Bromeliaceae
Pineapple	*Ananas comosus*	Bromeliaceae
Spanish moss	*Tillandsia usneoides*	Bromeliaceae
Buttonwood	*Conocarpus erectus*	Combretaceae

Common Name	Scientific Name	Plant family
Ceylon spinach	*Basella alba*	Basellaceae
Cuban oregano	*Coleus amboinicus*	Lamiaceae
Curry leaf tree	*Murraya koenigii*	Rutaceae
Echinacea	*Echinacea purpurea*	Asteraceae
Edible hibiscus	*Abelmoschus manihot*	Malvaceae
Elephant's ear	*Alocasia* species	Araceae
Florida native bald cypress	*Taxodium distichum*	Cupressaceae
Giant timber bamboo	*Bambusa oldhamii*	Poaceae
Goldenrod	*Solidago* species	Asteraceae
Gumbo limbo	*Bursera simaruba*	Burseraceae
Heliconia	*Heliconia* species	Heliconiaceae
Hibiscus	*Hibiscus rosa-sinensis* and cultivars	Malvaceae
Jojoba	*Simmondsia chinensis*	Buxaceae
Kalanchoe	*Kalanchoe* species	Crassulaceae
Luffa vine	*Luffa cylindrica*	Cucurbitaceae
Mangroves		
Black mangrove	*Avicennia germinans*	Verbenaceae
Red mangrove	*Rhizophora mangle*	Rhizophoraceae
White mangrove	*Laguncularia racemosa*	Combretaceae
Mistflower	*Conoclinium coelestinum*	Asteraceae
Orchids		
	Dendrobium lindleyi	Orchidaceae
	Laelia purpurata variety *werkhauseri*	Orchidaceae

Common Name	Scientific Name	Plant family
	Paphiopedilum malipoense	Orchidaceae
	Paphiopedilum rothschildianum	Orchidaceae
	Phalaenopsis schilleriana	Orchidaceae
	Renanthera imschootiana	Orchidaceae
Palms		
Cabbage palm	*Sabal palmetto*	Arecaceae
Date palm	*Phoenix* species	Arecaceae
Fishtail palm	*Caryotis mitis*	Arecaceae
Saw palmetto	*Serenoa repens*	Arecaceae
Triangle palm	*Dypsis decaryi*	Arecaceae
Papaya	*Carica papaya*	Caricaceae
Pineapple	*Ananas comosus*	Bromeliaceae
Plantain	*Musa x paradisiaca*	Musaceae
Sagalita	*Ceratostema silvicola*	Ericaceae
Seagrape	*Coccoloba uvifera*	Polygonaceae
Spanish moss	*Tillandsia usneoides*	Bromeliaceae
Sugar cane	*Saccharum officinarum*	Poaceae
Sweet potato	*Ipomoea batatas*	Convolvulaceae
Titan arum	*Amorphophallus titanum*	Araceae
Yucca	*Yucca* species	Agavaceae

Notes from My Visit...

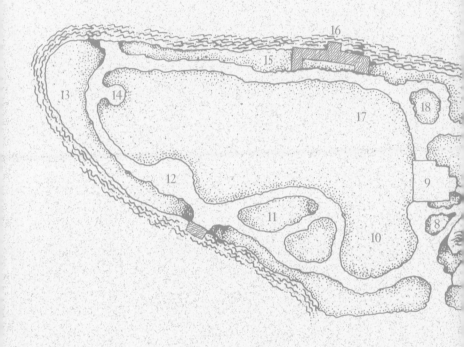

S E L B Y

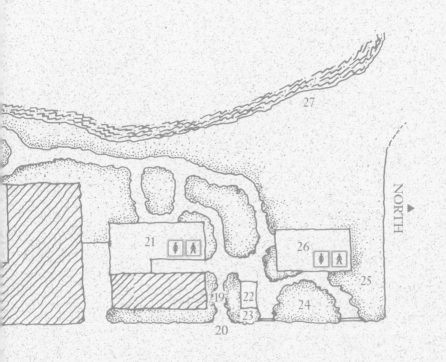

27

NORTH ►

21 🚹🚺

26 🚹🚺

25

19

22

23

24

20

RDENS